KT-161-168

HOME
Is Where My Heart Is

Smriti Halls   Alice Courtley

Andersen Press

Home is where my heart is.
Home is where I'm known.
Home is where I'm understood.
At home I'm not alone.

Home is where I'm learning,

Home is where I grow,

at home I am discovering

the things I need to know.

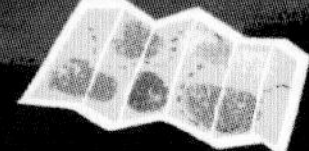

Home is where the battles
Of the day are lost and won.
Home is celebration!
Home is feeling fun.

Home is where I get to be what no one else can see.

Home is where I'm changing.

Home is where I'm ME.

Home brings out the worst in me . . . and the very best,

Home is where I challenge and put things to the test.

Home is outstretched arms where I shout and yell and rage,

Home is where I'm searching for the way I should behave.

Home is where I quarrel,
Home is where I fight,
Home is where I make mistakes
. . . and learn to put them right.

I know I'm FAR from home
When I'm not really being me,
When I'm trying to be the someone
Someone ELSE expects to see.

I know I'm far from home
When my voice feels out of place,
When I see in others' faces
That they do not like *my* face.

I know I'm far from home
When I feel I don't fit in,
When my words are stuck together,
And I feel strange inside my skin.

It's then I've lost my way,

But however far I roam . . .

Out there in the distance . . .

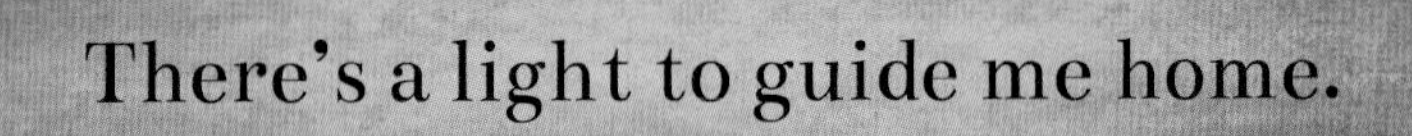

There's a light to guide me home.

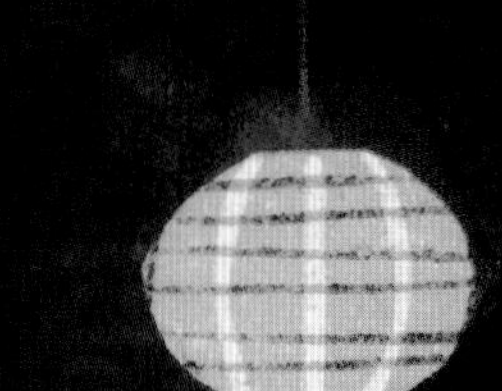

Home picks up the pieces,
Home finds every crack,
Every broken fragment,
And slowly glues me back.

At home I'll be restored,
At home I will get found,
Home is where I'm loved,
Home is solid ground.

Home is not a place,
It's the PEOPLE that love me.
Home is without borders,
Home is feeling free.

Home is small and safe,
Home is big and wide,
Home is joyful silence,
Sitting side by side.

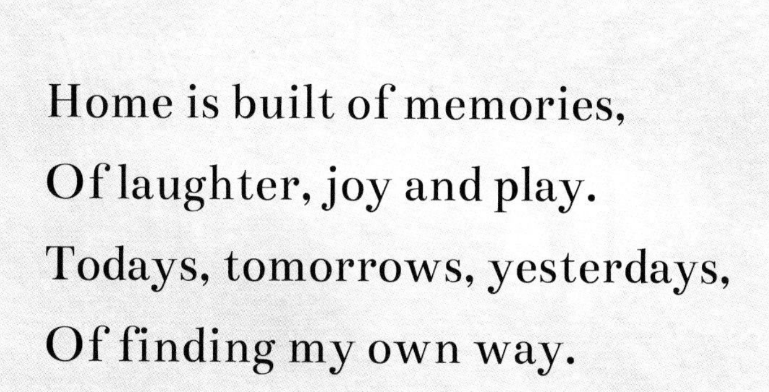

Home is built of memories,
Of laughter, joy and play.
Todays, tomorrows, yesterdays,
Of finding my own way.

Home gives me the strength to be the best that I can be,
And to share that strength and joy with **all** the others that I see.

So however far I travel,
Whichever way I turn,
I'll know where I have come from,
I know I will return.

For home could be a distant land,
Home could be right where I stand,
Simply being,
Hand in hand . . .
I'll know that I'm at home.

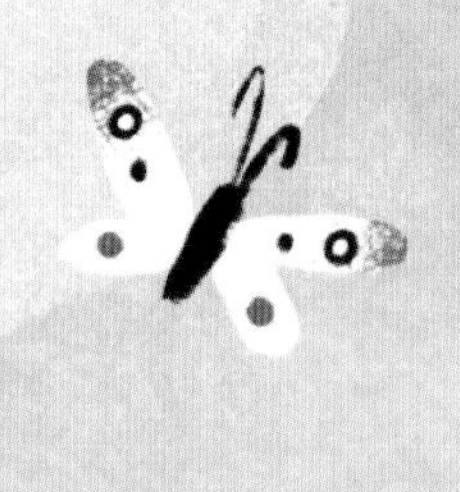

Yes, home is where my heart is,
It's with me where I go,
And whichever road I choose to take
Will always lead me home.

Also by Smriti Halls:

The Little Island

Bee You!

Find out more at
www.andersenpress.co.uk